Contents

The Kite Rider

Kites were invented in China many centuries ago, but they haven't always been used as toys. They often had very practical uses and were even used by the military. Kites were used to warn of invading enemies, send messages or test the wind before a ship set sail...

Gou Haoyou knew that his father's spirit lived among the clouds. For he had seen him go up there with a soul, and come down again without one. [...]

The ship on which his father Pei was about to set sail had a Tartar name now. Last season she had had a perfectly good Chinese name, but in an effort to curry
5   favour with the conquering barbarians, the captain had renamed her after the Khan's favourite wife: *Chabi*. Pei muttered gloomily about it. Her hull had been re-timbered, a new layer of wood hammered on over the old, so that she was beamier than the year before. 'It looks as if the Khan's wife has been eating too many cakes,' said Pei. He laughed and put a loving arm round Haoyou's shoulders.

10   'Impertinent dog,' said a voice close behind them, and the *Chabi's* First Mate took hold of Pei by his jacket and pushed him over the edge of an open hatchway.

It was no great way to fall, but Pei landed awkwardly, his leg twisted under him, and lay gasping on top of the sacks of rice which were the ship's provisions. Haoyou went to the hatchway and lowered one leg over its edge, going to the help of his father. But the First Mate took hold of him by the collar,
15   wrestled him along to the gangplank, and threw him off the ship.

Haoyou wondered whether to run home and tell his mother, or stay and see what happened. His father injured on the eve of a voyage? It was not good, not lucky. Lucky for Haoyou (who hated his father going away for months on a voyage), but not for the family dependent on his sailor's wages.

Haoyou decided his mother should know, and turned to run. But he found his way barred by the
20   corpulent bellies of the merchants mustering on the dockside. Word had gone out that the *Chabi* was testing the wind this morning, and it seemed as if every merchant in Dagu had hurried down to judge the omens for themselves. The prosperity of the whole voyage depended on how the 'wind-tester' behaved. Only if it flew well would they entrust their cargoes to the *Chabi*. If it flew badly, they would use some rival ship. [...]

25   A foreigner stood among the crowd — neither Chinese nor Mongol, but a tan-coloured man with eyes shaped like a horse or a dog. The Chinese man alongside him was explaining the process of testing the wind. [...]

Suddenly the tall foreigner with the horse eyes gave a cry. 'You did not tell me about the *man*!' [...]

The hurdle — a big square hatch-cover woven out of palm leaves — was being carried along the deck
30   by seven or eight sailors. The rope was already attached to it by a harness of four cords shackled to each of the four corners. Also bound to this giant kite was a man.

A cloth had been wrapped round his head, but now, as he twisted this way and that, struggling to break free, the cloth slipped down and Haoyou caught a clear glimpse of his face.

'*Father!*'

An abridged extract from *The Kite Rider* by Geraldine McCaughrean.

1 Read lines 1-2. What effect does this opening have on the reader?

....

....

2 marks

2 What does the change in the ship's name tell you
about what has happened since the last season?

....

....

2 marks

3 What does the word "corpulent" (line 20) mean? Check your answer in a dictionary.

....

1 mark

4 Explain why the wind-tester is important to the sailors and the merchants.

....

....

2 marks

5 Summarise how Haoyou's emotions change from line 12 to the end of the extract.

....

3 marks

....

Total
out of 10

....

Extra Activities

- Write a review of this extract. Did you enjoy it? Why or why not? Do you think you would like to read the rest of this book?

- Do you have any questions about this text? Write down five things you would like to ask the author.

- Imagine if you were at the dock and saw Haoyou's father on the kite. What would your reaction be? Write about how you would feel and what you would do.

- The sailors on the *Chabi* want to test the wind to judge the omens for their voyage. Create an advertisement for the *Chabi* that contains a prediction for the voyage. Your aim is to convince the merchants that they should use this ship for their cargo instead of a rival one.

Pair of Glasses Mistaken for Art

Modern art can be unusual and thought-provoking, and artists often use their work to make a statement about the world we live in. However, some critics claim that modern art requires little talent. This newspaper article reports on an incident in a modern art gallery in America...

Pair of glasses left on US gallery floor mistaken for art

Teenager leaves spectacles on floor of San Francisco's Museum of Modern Art as a prank, leading some to think they were an exhibit.

The feeling of slight dissatisfaction that can come
5 with visiting a modern art gallery is a universal one, best articulated* as "I could have done that".

A pair of US teenagers have beaten artists at their own game, pulling off a successful prank at the San Francisco Museum of Modern Art earlier this week.

10 While Kevin Nguyen, 16, and TJ Khayatan, 17, were impressed with much of the art on display on their visit on Saturday, they questioned the artistic merits of some exhibits.

Could they do better?

15 Khayatan put Nguyen's glasses on the floor below an official-looking piece of paper to see how it would be received by gallery-goers.

The work seemed to hit a chord with the public, striking in its simplicity, yet — probably — a
20 challenging commentary on the limits of individual perception.

Khayatan told BuzzFeed News that people gathered around the exhibit to view it and take photographs. He, in turn, took photographs of them admiring his
25 work and later posted them to Twitter, where they went viral.

Nguyen shared images, too, noting the awkwardness of having to retrieve his glasses before they moved on in the museum.

30 Nguyen told Guardian Australia he and Khayatan were surprised by the reception.

"We thought it would only get maybe at most a couple hundred retweets, but hey, I have a pair of famous glasses on my face every day now!"

35 The "social experiment" immortalised in a Twitter moment* — a commemoration of art in the digital age, you might say.

Nguyen said he had no intention of selling his now internet-famous eyewear — but he had an
40 alternative idea.

"My glasses are Burberry, so a sponsorship would be nice," he joked.

Asked how he interpreted the "art piece", he suggested "the deeper meaning" could be about
45 perception: "Anything in life can be art as long as you provide the insight and help people see what you see."

Copyright Guardian News & Media Ltd 2017

Glossary

articulated — explained   immortalised in a Twitter moment — made famous on Twitter

---

1 Explain in your own words why some visitors to modern art galleries might feel dissatisfied.

....

....

2 marks

2 Why do you think the author chose to include the word "probably" in line 19?

....

....

2 marks

3 Why do you think the prank was described as a "social experiment" (line 35)?

....

....

2 marks

4 How do you think the people who photographed the glasses on the floor might have felt when they found out it was a joke? Explain your answer.

....

....

2 marks

5 Do you agree that "Anything in life can be art" (line 45)? Explain your answer.

....

....

Total
out of 10

2 marks

....

Extra Activities

- Discuss your answer to question 5 with a partner. What do you think art is? What qualities does something need to be considered a work of art? Does it need to make you feel a certain way? Do you and your partner agree about what makes something art?

- Write an interview with one of the gallery owners. Ask them what they think about the joke, and whether they would consider installing the glasses as a real art piece.

- What artwork would you like to see in your school? Write a letter to your head teacher explaining the type of art you would like to see, and why they should consider displaying it in the school.

Wind Cat

Robert Westall was a British author who loved cats, and owned between 60 and 70 over the course of his life. Jeoffrey was Westall's favourite cat. In this poem, Jeoffrey encounters the wind cat, an invisible foe who threatens to steal in through the cat flap one stormy night.

Jeoffrey will not go out tonight,
Hovers by the cat-flap, paw uplifted,
Eyes wide and wild ears pricked
Listening to wind-cat prowling the earth.

5   Wind-cat assaults the cat-flap violently
With invisible paws,
But does not come in,
Does not have a smell,
But spits savagely in Jeoffrey's face,
10 Then retires to leap through the garden
Tearing and smashing fearsomely

At Jeoffrey's trees,
Making Jeoffrey's fence
Creak violently;
15 Transmitting his terrible size,
Then is back, rattling the flap,
Spitting again, a fearsome show.

Yet Jeoffrey
Is not entirely convinced,
20 How can so great a creature have no smell
But the usual grass, earth and trees?
Jeoffrey suspects a con
Until the cat next door,
The usual cat-flap burglar,
25 Terror of the road,
Streaks past the window
Cowering to the earth,
Soaked, blown and beaten
By the wind-cat's paws.

30 Jeoffrey seems to shrug,
Retires to the lounge
To wash, by the fire
And guard the house against
An infinitely smaller wind-cat
35 Burgling down the chimney.
He knows his limitations,
That's his strength.

Robert Westall

1 Why do you think the poet chose to compare the storm to a cat?

....

....

☐ 2 marks

2 What impression do you get of the wind cat from lines 5-17?
How does the poet create this impression?

....

....

☐ 2 marks

3 What do lines 23-29 suggest about Jeoffrey's relationship with the cat next door?

....

....

☐ 2 marks

4 What can you tell about Jeoffrey's character from the poem? Explain your answer.

....

....

☐ 2 marks

5 This poem is written in free verse. How does this reflect the storm?

Poems written in free verse don't have a regular rhyme scheme or rhythm.

....

☐ 2 marks

....

....

Total out of 10 ☐

Extra Activities

- What other animal could you use to describe the wind? Write your own poem, using the animal of your choice.

- Write a new description of the wind cat, making him friendly and playful. How would this wind cat have changed the meaning of the original poem?

- Write an interview with Jeoffrey the cat. Ask him about the mysterious wind cat that visits on stormy nights. What does he think he looks like? Why does he think he wants to enter the house?

- Imagine that you are the wind cat. Write about what it is like to be locked out of the house.

The Secret Garden

The Secret Garden tells the story of Mary, a young girl whose parents have both died. Mary is sent to live with her uncle in a grand manor in a remote part of Yorkshire. In this extract, the manor's housekeeper, Mrs Medlock, collects Mary from the train station in London.

She thought Mrs Medlock the most disagreeable person she had ever seen, with her common, highly coloured face and her common fine bonnet. When the next day they set out on their journey to Yorkshire, she walked through the station to the railway carriage with her head up and trying to keep as far away from her as she could, because she did not want to seem to belong to her. It
5 would have made her angry to think people imagined she was her little girl.

But Mrs Medlock was not in the least disturbed by her and her thoughts. She was the kind of woman who would "stand no nonsense from young ones." At least, that is what she would have said if she had been asked. She had not wanted to go to London just when her sister Maria's daughter was going to be married, but she had a comfortable, well paid place as housekeeper
10 at Misselthwaite Manor and the only way in which she could keep it was to do at once what Mr Archibald Craven told her to do. She never dared even to ask a question.

"Captain Lennox and his wife died of the cholera," Mr Craven had said in his short, cold way. "Captain Lennox was my wife's brother and I am their daughter's guardian. The child is to be brought here. You must go to London and bring her yourself."

15 So she packed her small trunk and made the journey.

Mary sat in her corner of the railway carriage and looked plain and fretful. She had nothing to read or to look at, and she had folded her thin little black-gloved hands in her lap. Her black dress made her look yellower than ever, and her limp light hair straggled from under her black crepe hat.

"A more marred-looking young one I never saw in my life," Mrs Medlock thought. (Marred is a
20 Yorkshire word and means spoiled and pettish.) She had never seen a child who sat so still without doing anything; and at last she got tired of watching her and began to talk in a brisk, hard voice.

"I suppose I may as well tell you something about where you are going to," she said. "Do you know anything about your uncle?"

"No," said Mary.

25 "Never heard your father and mother talk about him?"

"No," said Mary frowning. She frowned because she remembered that her father and mother had never talked to her about anything in particular. Certainly they had never told her things.

"Eh!" Mrs Medlock said, "but you are like an old woman. Don't you care?"

"It doesn't matter" said Mary, "whether I care or not."

An adapted extract from *The Secret Garden* by Frances Hodgson Burnett.

1 What evidence is there in this extract that *The Secret Garden* is set in the past?

....

....

2 marks

2 Read lines 16-18. In what ways does Mary differ from a traditional storybook heroine?

....

....

2 marks

3 Describe Mrs Medlock's attitude towards Mary using examples from the text.

....

....

....

2 marks

4 Read line 29. What do you think Mary means by this?

....

....

2 marks

5 Think about the personalities of Mr Craven and Mary. In what ways are they similar?

....

2 marks

....

....

Total
out of 10

Extra Activities

- Imagine that you are Mary. Write a diary entry covering the events of the extract.

- How do you think Mr Craven will react to Mary when she arrives at Misselthwaite Manor? Write a short passage describing their first meeting.

- Mary is 10 years old, but Mrs Medlock compares her to "an old woman". Do you agree with Mrs Medlock? Explain your answer.

- Do you want to read more of this book? Write a paragraph explaining why or why not.

A Letter to The Explorers Club

The Explorers Club is a society dedicated to science and exploration. For many years, women weren't allowed to join the society, so Carl Sagan, an astronomer and astrophysicist, sent this letter to his fellow members, asking them to reconsider the acceptance of female members.

Dear Fellow Member of The Explorers Club:

Thank you for the opportunity to write to you about the admission of women to The Explorers Club. The human zest for exploration and discovery is the hallmark of our species and one of the secrets of our success. It is a tradition that goes back much further than the
5   76 proud years in which The Explorers Club has been in existence. When our organization was formed in 1905, men were preventing women from voting and from pursuing many occupations for which they are clearly suited. In the popular mind, exploration was not what women did. Even so, women had played a significant but unheralded* role in the history of exploration — in Africa in the Nineteenth Century, for example. Similarly, Lewis and
10   Clark were covered with glory, but Sacajewea, who guided them every inch of the way, was strangely forgotten. All institutions reflect the prejudices and conventions of their times, and when it was founded The Explorers Club necessarily reflected the attitudes of 1905. [...]

Today women are making extraordinary contributions in areas of fundamental interest to our organization. There are several women astronauts. The earliest footprints — 3.6 million
15   years old — made by a member of the human family have been found in a volcanic ash flow in Tanzania by Mary Leakey. Trailblazing studies of the behavior of primates in the wild have been performed by dozens of young women, each spending years with a different primate species. Jane Goodall's studies of the chimpanzee are the best known of these investigations which illuminate human origins. The undersea depth record is held by Sylvia
20   Earle. The solar wind was first measured in situ by Marcia Neugebauer, using the Mariner 2 spacecraft. The first active volcanos beyond the Earth were discovered on the Jovian* moon Io by Linda Morabito, using the Voyager 1 spacecraft. These examples of modern exploration and discovery could be multiplied a hundredfold. They are of true historical significance. If membership in The Explorers Club is restricted to men, the loss will be ours; we will only be
25   depriving ourselves. [...]

I do not believe that the primary function of our organization is to promote male bonding or to serve as a social club — although there is certainly room for both. I believe that the fundamental dedication of
30   the club is that stated on the masthead of every issue of The Explorers Club Newsletter: "To the conquest of the unknown and the advancement of knowledge." If this is our purpose, then admission should be open to all qualified members of the human species.

35   Cordially,

(Signed)

Carl Sagan

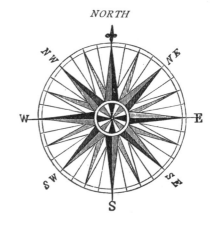

Glossary

unheralded — unnoticed	Jovian — belonging to the planet Jupiter

1 Is exploration and discovery humans' most important characteristic? Explain your answer.

....

....

2 marks

2 Carl writes that if membership is "restricted to men, the loss will be ours" (line 24).
In your own words, explain what you think he means by this statement.

....

....

2 marks

3 What techniques does Carl use to make his letter persuasive?

....

....

2 marks

4 Do you think Carl's letter would have convinced The Explorers
Club to accept female members? Explain your answer.

....

....

2 marks

5 Why do you think Carl uses the phrase "all qualified members of
the human species" on line 34 instead of "all men and women"?

....

....

2 marks

....

....

Total
out of 10

Extra Activities

*   Compose a response to Carl's letter from the other members of The Explorers Club. Do they agree with his argument or not? What action are they going to take next?

*   Discuss with a partner how you might feel if you were one of the women that Carl talks about in his letter, but were not allowed to join The Explorers Club. Would you want to be a member of the club?

*   Write an article for The Explorers Club newsletter about one of the women mentioned in Carl's letter.

*   A motto of The Explorers Club is "To the conquest of the unknown and the advancement of knowledge". Design a logo for the club, focused on this statement.

Miss Peregrine's Home for Peculiar Children

Miss Peregrine's Home for Peculiar Children is a fantasy novel about a boy called Jacob who encounters a group of children with supernatural abilities. In this extract, Jacob visits an abandoned children's home in Wales — a place his grandfather had a special connection to.

A vast lunar bog stretched away into the mist from either side of the path, just brown grass and tea-colored water as far as I could see, featureless but for the occasional mound of piled-up stones. It ended abruptly at a forest of skeletal trees, branches spindling up like the tips of wet paintbrushes, and for a while the path became so lost beneath fallen trunks and carpets of ivy that navigating it was a matter

5 of faith. I wondered how an elderly person like Miss Peregrine would ever be able to negotiate such an obstacle course. *She must get deliveries*, I thought, though the path looked like it hadn't seen a footprint in months, if not years.

I scrambled over a giant trunk slick with moss, and the path took a sharp turn. The trees parted like a curtain and suddenly there it was, cloaked in fog, looming atop a weed-choked hill. The house. I

10 understood at once why the boys had refused to come.

My grandfather had described it a hundred times, but in his stories the house was always a bright, happy place — big and rambling, yes, but full of light and laughter. What stood before me now was no refuge from monsters but a monster itself, staring down from its perch on the hill with vacant hunger. Trees burst forth from broken windows and skins of scabrous* vine gnawed at the walls like anti-bodies attacking a

15 virus — as if nature itself had waged war against it — but the house seemed unkillable, resolutely upright despite the wrongness of its angles and the jagged teeth of sky visible through sections of collapsed roof.

I tried to convince myself that it was possible someone could still live there, run-down as it was. Such things weren't unheard of where I came from — a falling-down wreck on the edge of town, curtains permanently drawn, that would turn out to have been home to some ancient recluse who'd been surviving

20 on ramen* and toenail clippings since time immemorial, though no one realises it until a property appraiser or an overly ambitious census taker barges in to find the poor soul returning to dust in a La-Z-Boy*. People get too old to care for a place, their family writes them off for one reason or another — it's sad, but it happens. [...]

I came around back and saw my opportunity: a doorless doorway, bearded with vines, gaping and black; an

25 open mouth just waiting to swallow me. Just looking at it made my skin crawl, but I hadn't come halfway around the world just to run away screaming at the sight of a scary house. I thought of all the horrors Grandpa Portman had faced in his life, and felt my resolve harden. If there was anyone to find inside, I would find them. I mounted the crumbling steps and crossed the threshold.

An abridged extract from *Miss Peregrine's Home for Peculiar Children* by Ransom Riggs.

Glossary		
scabrous — rough	ramen — noodles	La-Z-Boy — a reclining chair

1 Find and copy a simile from lines 1-7.

....

1 mark

2 Do you find the description of the house in lines 11-16 effective? Explain your answer.

....

....

2 marks

3 Using your own words, summarise Jacob's thoughts in lines 17-23.

....

....

2 marks

4 What do lines 24-28 tell you about Jacob's character?

....

....

2 marks

5 What impression do you get of nature in this extract?
Use examples from the text to explain your answer.

....

3 marks

....

Total

....
out of 10

Extra Activities

• Underline all the similes in this extract. Circle all the metaphors. Choose a simile or a metaphor that you find particularly effective and explain why.

• Imagine that you are visiting the house with Jacob. Does the house scare you? Do you want to find out what is inside? Write a conversation that you might have with Jacob about whether or not you should enter the building.

• Rewrite the description of the house and its surroundings as Jacob's grandfather would have seen it, using similes, metaphors and personification. Make the house seem as friendly as possible.

• Write a description of a child with special powers. What do they look like? What are their powers?

Through My Eyes

Until the 1950s, many US schools were segregated — black and white children were educated separately. From 1954, this began to change and US schools were slowly integrated. In 1960, six-year-old Ruby Bridges was the first black child to attend an all-white school in New Orleans.

When we left school that first day, the crowd outside was even bigger and louder than it had been in the morning. There were reporters and film cameras and people everywhere. I guess the police couldn't keep them behind the barricades. It seemed to take us a long time to get to the marshals' car.

5 Later on I learned there had been protestors in front of the two integrated schools the whole day. They wanted to be sure white parents would boycott the school and not let their children attend. Groups of high school boys, joining the protestors, paraded up and down the street and sang new verses to old hymns. Their favourite was "Battle Hymn of the Republic," in which they changed the chorus to "Glory, glory, segregation, the South
10 will rise again." Many of the boys carried signs and said awful things. [...]

Everybody was glad for time out at Thanksgiving, including me. Even so, the stress didn't go away completely. The owners of the small grocery store at the end of the block suddenly told my family to stay away. Because we were a part of school integration, the white owners no longer wanted our business.

15 My grandparents telephoned from Mississippi to say they were afraid for us. [...]

My parents didn't tell us if they were afraid for their lives, but I knew my father was worried about how to make a living. The garage where he worked had fired him because I was going to a white school.

Financial help was on its way, fortunately, and it came through the U.S. mail. People
20 from around the country sent gifts and money. They knew what was happening in New Orleans because of television news programs, as well as magazine and newspaper articles. Many Americans wanted to encourage us. The money made a big difference to my family, and it kept coming for months. [...]

Near the end of the year, Mrs. Henry and I finally had company. A few white children
25 began coming back to school, and I got an opportunity to visit with them once or twice. Even though these children were white, I still knew nothing about racism or integration. I had picked up bits and pieces over the months from being around adults and hearing them talk, but nothing was clear to me. The light dawned one day when a little white boy refused to play with me. [...] At that moment, it all made sense to me. I finally realized
30 that everything had happened because I was black. I remember feeling a little stunned. It was all about the colour of my skin.

An abridged extract from Through My Eyes by Ruby Bridges.

1 Read line 2. Why do you think reporters and film cameras were present?

....

....

2 marks

2 What does the word "boycott" (line 6) mean? Check your answer in a dictionary.

....

1 mark

3 How did people make life difficult for Ruby's family? Why do you think they did this?

....

....

....

3 marks

4 Why do you think people sent money to Ruby and her family?

....

....

2 marks

5 Ruby states that she visited the white children "once or twice" (line 25). What does this tell you about the reality of her 'integrated' school?

....

2 marks

....

Total out of 10

....

Extra Activities

• Write a news report about the first day that Ruby attended the school. Try to imagine the scene that day and how Ruby might have reacted to it all.

• Imagine that you are one of the people supporting Ruby and her family by sending them money and gifts. Write a letter to accompany your parcel expressing your support.

• Think about everything Ruby had to go through just to receive a good education. Do you think she was brave to attend the school? Why do you think her story is important? Write a paragraph explaining your thoughts.

Myths from Different Cultures

'The Weaving Contest' is a version of a myth from Ancient Greece. It is about a girl who challenges the goddess of wisdom, craft and war. The second myth is a tale from the Yoruba religion — a belief system practised in and around Togo, Benin and the south west of Nigeria.

The Weaving Contest

Arachne was the most talented weaver in all of Greece. People loved to watch her spin, ingeniously manipulating the wool to create scenes that took their breath away. They praised her work and gave thanks to the goddess of craft for blessing Arachne with such a wonderful skill. This praise was a great honour, but Arachne was proud and foolish.

5　"My skills weren't given to me by Athena," she proclaimed angrily. "My work is greater than anything she could ever produce!"

Athena soon heard about Arachne and her talents. One day, she cloaked herself in rags to hide her identity and paid the girl a visit. When she saw Arachne weave, Athena was truly impressed. "Your weaving is exquisite, child," she said, "but you must not grow conceited. No mortal can produce work
10　as great as the gods can."

Again, Arachne flew into a wild rage. "I can!" she shouted. "If Athena were here, I would challenge her to a weaving contest, and I would win."

At this, Athena revealed herself. "I accept your challenge," she said, and the pair began their work.

Athena's tapestry sprang to life and she depicted the gods in all their glory. Arachne's work was even
15　more magnificent — but she had made the gods appear disorderly and corrupt. Athena was enraged that Arachne would use her talent to create such unflattering images. She touched her hand to Arachne's head, filling it with shame. Arachne became so ashamed at her behaviour that she began to wither, shrinking down and transforming into a spider. She and her descendants have been weaving ever since.

Olodumare's Messenger

Before the land was made, there existed only the sky above and the sea below. Olodumare, king of the gods, ruled the skies while Olokun ruled over the watery depths. But Olokun was jealous of Olodumare's power, and believed she should be the ruler of the gods. One day, she challenged Olodumare to a weaving contest.

Olodumare knew that no weaving talents in the world could equal Olokun's, so he devised a cunning plan
5　and sent the Chameleon to Olokun's kingdom as his messenger.

Olokun was awaiting Olodumare's messenger in a shimmering gown of many beautiful colours and ornate patterns. She was confident that the king of the gods would never be able to match her talents. However, when she greeted the messenger she found he was wearing a gown identical to her own.

She retreated to her chamber, and adorned herself with another beautiful robe that sparkled like the
10　moonlight on the surface of her kingdom. Yet when she returned, she found the messenger had also changed, and again his outfit was equal to hers. She retreated once more, and was once more matched. Olokun changed her outfit five more times, her robes increasing in splendour with each change, but every time the Chameleon's robes changed with her own.

Finally, Olokun accepted defeat and forfeited the contest. She knew that she could never compete with the
15　grandeur of the great king, when her own most splendid clothes had been matched by his lowly messenger.

The Chameleon returned to Olodumare, and Olokun never challenged him again.

By Zoe Fenwick.

1 Do you think Athena was right to punish Arachne? Explain your answer.

....
....
2 marks

2 Do you think it was fair that Olokun lost the contest? Explain your answer.

....
....
2 marks

3 Compare the personalities of Athena and Olodumare. Give one similarity and one difference.

....
....
....
2 marks

4 Do you think the messages of the two myths are similar or different? Explain your answer.

....
....
2 marks

5 Think about the structure of these two myths. In what ways are they similar?

....
2 marks

....
....

Total
out of 10

Extra Activities

- Write a different ending to the first myth, rewriting from line 13 onwards.

- Discuss your answers to questions 4 and 5 with a partner. Are you surprised that these two myths from different cultures are so similar? Discuss why there might be similarities between them.

- Which myth did you prefer? Write a few sentences explaining your choice.

- Both these myths contain animals with special skills. Write a short myth of your own which features an animal that has a special skill.

Year 6 Stretch — Targeted Comprehension

Journey to the Centre of the Earth

Journey to the Centre of the Earth follows the adventures of Professor Otto Lidenbrock and his nephew Axel, who narrates the story. After deciphering a cryptic message that leads them to Iceland, they meet a guide named Hans, and the three start a dangerous underground journey.

Our real journey had finally begun. Until now, our courage and determination had been enough to overcome all the difficulties we faced. We were sometimes tired, but that was about the worst of it. Now we were going to face unknown and terrifying dangers.

5 I had not yet dared to peer into the horrible abyss that I was about to enter. However, the point of no return had finally arrived and I had to make a decision. This was my last chance to turn my back on the whole foolish adventure.

Gingerly, I approached the edge of the gaping hole.

It stretched out in front of me, at least a hundred feet wide. I leaned warily on a rock which jutted out from the edge, and looked down. My hair stood on end, my teeth chattered, I
10 shook uncontrollably. I felt completely off balance, and my head was in a sort of whirl. I felt a pull from my core towards the endless darkness that lay below. I was about to fall head first into the black void when I was drawn back by the firm and powerful hand of our guide, Hans.

I had only looked into this astonishing shaft for a few short moments, but it had been enough to give me a good idea of its physical structure. Its sides, despite being almost completely
15 vertical, offered numerous nooks and ledges which would help us make our way down into the depths. In fact, it was a sort of wild and savage staircase, without bannister or fence.

We fastened a rope to a sturdy boulder at the surface and began our descent. Hans went first, my uncle followed, and I went last. Our progress was made in absolute silence — a silence broken only by the fall of pieces of rock, which broke from the jagged sides and fell
20 with a roar into the depths below.

At first, I allowed myself to slide downwards, holding the rope frantically with one hand and using the other to keep myself off the rocks. However, with every passing moment I was gripped by a growing fear that the rope would fail us, for it seemed far too fragile to support three grown men. Increasingly, therefore, I did my best not to put my full weight on the rope,
25 and instead clutched at the craggy rock face with desperate hands and feet.

After three hours of grim concentration, we seemed as far from the bottom of the well as when we set out. When I looked up, however, I could see that the hole through which we had entered was becoming ever smaller, letting in less and less light. We were entering the regions of eternal night.

30 And still we continued to descend!

An adapted extract from *Journey to the Centre of the Earth* by Jules Verne.

1 In your own words, summarise lines 8-12.

....

....

2 marks

2 Read line 16. Do you find this description of the shaft effective? Explain your answer.

....

....

2 marks

3 What does the narrator mean when he says "We were entering the regions of eternal night" (lines 28-29)?

....

....

2 marks

4 Do you think the narrator is brave? Explain your answer.

....

....

2 marks

5 Did this extract make you want to read more of *Journey to the Centre of the Earth*? Explain your answer.

....

2 marks

....

Total

.... out of 10

Extra Activities

- Imagine Professor Lidenbrock and Axel meeting Hans and telling him about their plans for the journey. Write a script for the conversation. How do you think Hans might react when the Professor and Axel explain that they want to travel to the centre of the Earth?

- What might be waiting for the group at the bottom of the shaft? Write a list of five ideas, then discuss them with a partner. Together, pick one idea and write a description of it.

- The extract says that the trio have already faced some difficulties on their journey. What do you think these difficulties might have been? Write a story about one of the problems they encountered and how they overcame it.

The Real Junk Food Project

Every year in the UK, around 10 million tonnes of food is thrown away. Lots of this food is still edible. If it were used instead of being thrown away, it could provide nutritious meals for schoolchildren and help to reduce the number of people who have to rely on foodbanks.

THE REAL JUNK FOOD PROJECT: TACKLING HUNGER AND POVERTY WITH FOOD WASTE

"In a word, it's — insane!" declares Adam Smith, chef and founder of The Real Junk Food Project. "We're working with bigger volumes of food than I ever could have imagined, delivering to more people than
5 we've ever encountered before."

This is not hyperbole*. Smith […] started The Real Junk Food Project (TRJFP) in December 2013 when, appalled by vast quantities of perfectly edible food being binned in the UK while spiralling numbers of
10 Brits rely on handouts from foodbanks, he started a cafe in Leeds making meals from ingredients dumped in skips outside supermarkets, shops and restaurants, and let people pay whatever they could afford. His idea has gone supernova*: TRJFP has now fed half
15 a million people globally, with 30 cafes in Leeds, a total of 95 across the UK and a growing international presence. […]

Global statistics on food waste and hunger are so monumental they can be hard to digest: one billion
20 people go hungry every day while 1.3 billion tonnes of food is wasted annually. But given the opportunity to make local changes that have a tangible* impact, growing armies of people are seizing it. […]

Last April TRJFP partnered with 30 schools in Leeds
25 to redirect six tonnes of food that became free meals for 12,000 pupils, and set up market stall shops selling food on a 'pay as you feel' basis. They were an instant success, stalls being used not just by low-income kids or parents but teachers too.

30 Come September, Smith aims to equip 290 English schools with the know-how to adapt this model, doing assemblies, workshops, education on expiry dates and cooking workshops.

"We can't afford to not move fast," Smith continues.
35 "Hunger is a barrier to learning and we're helping break that down. We're getting levels of engagement and educational outcomes that we didn't envisage*."

Teachers reported improvement in reading and writing ("some children wrote letters to David
40 Cameron* asking why so much food was being wasted," Smith says with pride), better behaviour and reaching parents reticent* to engage with schools. "Everybody needs to eat. And when you've got 200 kilos of food from Marks and Spencer, you've got
45 kids walking around eating beautiful organic cherries or blackberries, or food that they've never seen or heard of before.

"It needs to go national if not international as soon as possible," he adds, pointing out that councils — and
50 schools — keep all their market stall takings, some buying toasters for classrooms, others tablets for parents to do job-searches.

In an ideal future Smith says "if we have a whole generation of children growing up eating food
55 that would've gone to waste, understanding the environmental impact, about food provision, providing for themselves, then we have a generation that no longer depends on foodbanks. In 10 to 15 years' time we could have a massive impact on the
60 reduction of foodbanks across this country."

An abridged extract from *www.bigissue.com*

Glossary

hyperbole — deliberate exaggeration	supernova — a bright exploding star	tangible — real
envisage — predict	David Cameron — UK Prime Minister from 2010-2016	reticent — reluctant

1 Do you think The Real Junk Food Project cafes are a good idea? Explain your answer.

....

....

2 marks

2 Look at line 19. Why do you think the author chose the phrase "hard to digest"?

....

....

2 marks

3 The Real Junk Food Project market stalls aren't just used by families with low incomes. What does this suggest?

....

....

2 marks

4 In your own words, summarise the impact that The Real Junk Food Project has had on schools.

....

....

2 marks

5 What is Adam's vision for the future? Do you think he feels optimistic about achieving it?

....

2 marks

....

....
Total
out of 10

Extra Activities

- Adam has decided to come to your school to give an assembly about his work. Write down five questions that you would like to ask him.

- Write a letter to your local supermarket asking them to donate their food waste to your school. Make sure you explain how the donations would help the school and the local community.

- Imagine that you are a food critic eating at one of The Real Junk Food Project cafes. Write a review of the food that explains how much money you would pay for it.

- Create a menu for one of The Real Junk Food Project cafes. Try to think of imaginative names for the dishes — and remember that customers can choose the price.

The Three Musketeers

The Three Musketeers is a novel by Alexandre Dumas, published in 1844. It is set in the 1620s, and follows a young man called d'Artagnan on his quest to become a member of the King's guard — the famous Musketeers. This extract is from a modern stage adaptation of the story.

The stage is empty and the lights are up. Suddenly, with a loud cry, two men burst into view in a furious sword fight. They start off fighting in the aisle of the theatre, then onto the stage. As they fight, the set is formed around them.

Outside a farmhouse in Gascony in the spring of 1625. The men continue to fight furiously. One of them (d'Artagnan) is 18 years old, the other (his Father) in his late forties. At first, one has the advantage, then the other. At last, the
5 *Father gets the advantage, disarms d'Artagnan, and holds the point of his sword at the young man's throat. D'Artagnan quails for a moment… then breaks into a smile.*

D'Artagnan: Father, how do you *do* that?! It's like a magic trick.

Father: Misdirection, son. Get your opponent to lose his focus, then move like lightning. Hey! Snap! Ha!

He again disarms d'Artagnan — taking him by surprise — and holds the sword at his throat briefly before removing it.

10 If you want to conquer worlds, concentrate. Draw your mind to the centre, like a magnet. Couple that with common sense, a will to succeed and, above all, a kind heart, and you'll be a great man as I predict.

D'Artagnan: Like my father

They embrace.

Father: It's time you were going.

15 D'Artagnan: Did you leave home at my age, sir?

Father: Yes, and for the same reason. To be a musketeer.

D'Artagnan: I dream about it every night. Fighting duels, defending the King, standing up to the Cardinal and his —

Father: Stop.

D'Artagnan: What?

20 Father: Never say that. You do not want Cardinal Richelieu as your enemy. […] Just do your duty and never *ever* engage the Cardinal directly. Is that clear?

D'Artagnan: [*Grudgingly*] Yes, sir. Unless he starts it first…

Father shakes his head, thinking 'Children!'

Father: Here. Take my sword. You'll need it.

25 D'Artagnan: [*Overwhelmed*] Father…

Father: Use it well, to fight for justice. For justice, like mercy, is divine and deserves your courage. Always stand up for what you believe in. Never back down unless you're wrong. If a man insults you, turn the other cheek. If he insults you again, kill him. Make courage your watchword. But courage is more than arms and legs. It takes courage to be yourself, so do it. Above all things, live a life of honour.
30 Honour the people you love, the ideals you cherish and the man inside you.

D'Artagnan: I promise.

Father: Now a few parting gifts and you're on your way. Twenty-five crowns. Say nothing. I wish it were more. Second, a letter, recommending you to Monsieur de Treville.

D'Artagnan: Your old friend.

35 Father: Now Captain of the Musketeers.

D'Artagnan: Oh I know! They say that he's fought hundreds of duels in the King's service. They say the King relies on him for everything. They say —

Father: 'They say, they say.' He was my *schoolmate*. We were lads together. And he will help you thread the needle of Paris. Now keep this safe.

An abridged extract from *The Three Musketeers* by Alexandre Dumas, adapted by Ken Ludwig.

1 Look at lines 1-2. What difficulties might there be in staging this part of the play?

....

....

2 marks

2 How does the opening fight contrast with the dialogue between the characters? How do you think this sudden change would make the audience feel?

....

....

2 marks

3 Do you think the father gives d'Artagnan good advice in lines 26-30? Explain your answer.

....

....

2 marks

4 Find and copy a metaphor from lines 31-39.

....

1 mark

5 Explain what this extract reveals about the relationship between d'Artagnan and his father. Use examples from the text to support your answer.

....

....

3 marks

....

Total out of 10

....

Extra Activities

- Imagine that you have seen this scene performed on stage. Write a review of the performance — include whether or not you enjoyed the scene and any aspects you feel could be improved.

- D'Artagnan's father wants him to leave home and join the Musketeers. How would this scene be different if his father wanted him to stay? Write a script for their discussion.

- The Musketeers were founded by the French King Louis XIII in 1622. It was their job to protect the king. Create a poster advertising for people to apply to join the Musketeers. Remember to use persuasive language and think about what might make someone want to sign up.

Penguins Around the World

There are around 17 different species of penguin in the world — and not all of them live in Antarctica. This extract gives some details about two different types of penguin, which are distinctive for either their eye-catching headgear or their rather unusual choice of habitat...

Macaroni Penguins

Showing off with their bright tufts of yellow feathers, macaroni penguins are easy to spot against the rocky, frozen landscape of their broad kingdom, which stretches from Antarctica, through
5   numerous Subantarctic islands*, and all the way to the southernmost tip of South America. The penguins' tufts, starting from just above the eyes and beak, are akin to extravagantly styled eyebrows, fanning out magnificently across the backs of their heads.

However, the macaronis' talents are not limited to their expert hair styling — these birds are also
10   highly skilled disco dancers, putting on flamboyant shows (known as courtship displays) to try to attract a mate. Dipping and shaking their heads like they're the kings of the dance floor, macaronis take full advantage of their luscious locks to impress their partners. As they whirl their golden plumage, the penguins throw back their heads and screech at the top of their lungs. This clamorous call sounds like the cackle of a gleeful witch, piercing the air as other penguins gurgle around them.

15   During the breeding season, macaroni penguins pile onto the shore in colonies of up to 100 000, and each pair hurriedly claims a patch of rock to squash their nest onto. With so many other penguins around to cramp their style, conflicts are common. The miniature combatants lock beaks with each other in vicious wrestling competitions, or swipe at each other with their flippers in order to keep other penguins off their turf. Ouch!

20 ### African Penguins

Far from the icy terrain that many penguins call home, African penguins splash through the surf on sandy shores. These rule breakers have swapped the biting winds of Antarctica for the sweltering heat of Africa's south-west coast. Found on beaches, and sporting bright pink glands above their eyes, these holidaying
25   penguins have the permanent air of tourists who forgot their sun cream.

However, living the high life in the African sun brings some unique challenges. To prevent themselves and their eggs from frying in the heat, these adventurous birds must seek out shady sites for their nests. Piles of their own droppings, called guano, make the perfect place for these penguins to nest. Sadly, a lot of this precious guano has
30   been grabbed by greedy humans to fertilise crops, so the penguins often have to bed down elsewhere. They'll happily nest under rocks and bushes, but when all the best spots have been snapped up, many penguins have no choice but to incubate their eggs out in the open. Baking in the sun, the parched birds must brave temperatures of up to 30°C while they wait for their eggs to hatch — yikes!

By Zoe Fenwick.

> **Glossary**
> Subantarctic islands — islands just outside of the Antarctic region

1 Find and copy a metaphor from lines 9-10. Why do you think the author chose to describe macaroni penguins in this way?

....

....

2 marks

2 Identify two techniques used in the phrase "This clamorous call sounds like the cackle of a gleeful witch" (lines 13-14).

....

2 marks

3 Read lines 15-19. What impression do you get of macaroni penguins from this paragraph? Explain your answer.

....

....

2 marks

4 In your own words, summarise lines 26-33.

....

....

2 marks

5 This text uses a lot of informal language. Why do you think the author writes in this way?

....

2 marks

....

....

Total
out of 10

Extra Activities

- If you were making a nature documentary, which of these species of penguin would you want to film? Write an argument for one of the species, explaining why it is the best choice.

- Choose one paragraph from this extract and rewrite it using more formal language.

- Write a paragraph about your favourite animal in a similar style to this text. You could include where it lives, what it looks like and some interesting facts about it.

- Imagine that you have found some penguins living in an unexpected place. Write a letter to a wildlife magazine about your discovery. Include a description of where you discovered the penguins, and explain why it was so surprising. Think about how the penguins might have adapted to their new environment.

Anne of Green Gables

Anne of Green Gables was written by Canadian author Lucy Maud Montgomery and published in 1908. The novel focuses on Anne, an orphan who is sent to live with Marilla Cuthbert and her brother, Matthew. In this extract, Marilla introduces Anne to her neighbour, Mrs Rachel.

"It's a great responsibility you've taken on yourself," said Mrs Rachel, "especially when you've never had any experience with children. You don't know much about her or her real character, I suppose, and there's no guessing how a child like that will turn out. But I don't want to discourage you I'm sure, Marilla."

5 "I'm not feeling discouraged," was Marilla's dry response, "when I make up my mind to do a thing it stays made up. I suppose you'd like to see Anne. I'll call her in."

Anne came running in at once. She certainly was an odd-looking little creature in the short tight dress she had worn from the orphanage, below which her thin legs seemed ungracefully long. Her freckles were more numerous than ever; the wind had ruffled her hatless hair into over-brilliant disorder; it had

10 never looked redder than at that moment.

"Well, they didn't pick you for your looks, that's sure and certain," was Mrs Rachel's first comment. Mrs Rachel was one of those delightful and popular people who pride themselves on speaking their mind without fear or favour. "She's terrible skinny and plain, Marilla. Come here, child, and let me have a look at you. Goodness, did anyone ever see such freckles? And hair as red as carrots! Come

15 here, child, I say."

Anne "came there," but not exactly as Mrs Rachel expected. With one bound she crossed the kitchen floor and stood before Mrs Rachel, her face scarlet with anger, her lips quivering, and her whole slender form trembling from head to foot.

"I hate you," she cried in a choked voice, stamping her foot on the floor. "I hate you — I hate you —

20 I hate you —" a louder stamp with each statement of hatred. "How dare you call me skinny and ugly? How dare you say I'm freckled and redheaded? You are a rude, impolite, unfeeling woman!"

"Anne!" exclaimed Marilla in alarm.

But Anne continued to face Mrs Rachel, head up, eyes blazing, hands clenched, passionate indignation exhaling from her like an atmosphere.

25 "How dare you say such things about me?" she repeated furiously. "How would you like to have such things said about you? How would you like to be told that you are fat and clumsy and probably hadn't a spark of imagination in you? I don't care if I do hurt your feelings by saying so! I hope I hurt them. You have hurt mine worse than they were ever hurt before. And I'll never forgive you for it, never, never!"

30 Stamp! Stamp!

"Did anybody ever see such a temper!" exclaimed the horrified Mrs Rachel.

"Anne go to your room and stay there until I come up," said Marilla, recovering her powers of speech with difficulty.

Anne, bursting into tears, rushed to the hall door, slammed it until the tins on the porch wall outside

35 rattled in sympathy, and fled through the hall and up the stairs like a whirlwind.

An adapted extract from *Anne of Green Gables* by Lucy Maud Montgomery.

1 Read lines 1-4. Do you think Mrs Rachel agrees with Marilla's decision to adopt Anne? Explain your answer.

....

....

2 marks

2 Find and copy a simile from lines 11-15.

....

1 mark

3 The author describes Mrs Rachel as "delightful and popular" (line 12). Do you think this is an accurate description? Explain your answer.

....

....

2 marks

4 What effect does the end of the extract have on the reader? Explain your answer.

....

....

2 marks

5 Explain what this extract tells you about Anne's personality.

....

....

3 marks

....

....

Total
out of 10

Extra Activities

• Think about how Anne and Mrs Rachel behave in this extract. Do you think their behaviour is similar or different? Write a paragraph to explain your answer.

• Imagine that you are Anne. Write a letter of apology to Mrs Rachel. Think about how Anne might write the letter and whether or not she would really be sorry for her actions.

• How might you feel if someone spoke to you in the way Mrs Rachel spoke to Anne? Write a list of ways you could deal with the situation without losing your temper.

Poems about the Sea

Epes Sargent spent time at sea when he was a boy. He wrote 'A Life on the Ocean Wave' after seeing ships in the harbour. John Masefield was sent to train on a ship when he was a teenager. His experiences of long voyages to the Americas inspired him to write about the sea.

A Life on the Ocean Wave

A life on the ocean wave,
          A home on the rolling deep,
Where the scattered waters rave,
          And the winds their revels keep!
5   Like an eagle caged, I pine
          On this dull, unchanging shore:
Oh! give me the flashing brine,
          The spray and the tempest's roar!

Once more on the deck I stand
10   Of my own swift-gliding craft:
Set sail! farewell to the land!
          The gale follows fair abaft*.
We shoot through the sparkling foam
          Like an ocean-bird set free; —
15   Like the ocean-bird, our home
          We'll find far out on the sea.

The land is no longer in view,
          The clouds have begun to frown;
But with a stout vessel and crew,
20   We'll say, Let the storm come down!
And the song of our hearts shall be,
          While the winds and the waters rave,
A home on the rolling sea!
          A life on the ocean wave!

Epes Sargent

Glossary
abaft — behind the ship
spume — froth
whetted — sharpened

Sea Fever

I must go down to the seas again, to the lonely sea and the sky,
And all I ask is a tall ship and a star to steer her by,
And the wheel's kick and the wind's song and the white sail's shaking,
And a gray mist on the sea's face, and a gray dawn breaking.

5   I must go down to the seas again, for the call of the running tide
Is a wild call and a clear call that may not be denied;
And all I ask is a windy day with the white clouds flying,
And the flung spray and the blown spume*, and the sea-gulls crying.

I must go down to the seas again, to the vagrant gypsy life,
10 To the gull's way and the whale's way, where the wind's like a whetted* knife;
And all I ask is a merry yarn from a laughing fellow-rover,
And quiet sleep and a sweet dream when the long trick's over.

John Masefield

1 What does the title 'Sea Fever' suggest about the narrator's relationship with the sea?

....

....

2 marks

2 Do you think the narrator of Sargent's poem has a similar relationship with the sea? Explain your answer.

....

....

2 marks

3 Why do you think these poems both use repetition?

....

1 mark

4 Which senses does Masefield use in 'Sea Fever'? What effect does this have on the reader?

....

....

....

3 marks

5 Which of these poems do you prefer? Why?

....

2 marks

....

Total
out of 10

....

Extra Activities

- What techniques can you identify in these poems? Underline examples, using a different colour for each technique. Write your own poem about the sea, using some of the techniques you have identified.

- Imagine that you are one of the sea-gulls or ocean birds described in the poems. Describe the view of the ship, sea and shore below as you soar in the sky.

- Epes Sargent and John Masefield both used their experiences of travelling on ships to help them write about the sea. Would you like to travel on a ship for a long voyage? Make a list of the pros and cons of sea travel.

The Tempest

The Tempest was written in around 1610, and was one of the last plays William Shakespeare wrote. It is set on an island off the coast of Italy. In this scene, Caliban is collecting wood for his master, the sorcerer Prospero, when he stumbles across a man who has been shipwrecked.

Lightning struck just off the shore as Caliban flung down the burden of wood he had been carrying and began to curse his master. Prospero controlled many of the magical spirits that lived on the island, and often sent them to torment Caliban while he was working. They would pinch him, scare him with illusions or throw him into bogs. Sometimes, the frightful spirits would light flaming
5   torches in the darkness to lead him the wrong way, or pull faces and chatter at him like apes. Each time they would plague him with new tricks — even turning themselves into hedgehogs which spiked his feet as he walked, or transforming into snakes and wrapping themselves around him to hiss in his ears.

Caliban cursed once more, and a deafening rumble of thunder filled the air. Thinking that his
10   master must have heard his complaints, he began desperately trying to hoist the wood back onto his shoulders, trembling with fear. At that moment, he saw a terrible spirit staggering towards him. It had strange, brightly coloured skin, and bells hung from the top of its head. Caliban was terrified — he was convinced that Prospero had sent this creature to punish him. He dropped to the ground and covered himself with his dirty old cloak, hoping that if he laid still, the spirit wouldn't spot him.

15   Caliban had never seen a man who was not his master, so he didn't recognise the brightly coloured outfit of the King's fool. The creature Caliban had seen was not a spirit at all, but the jester Trinculo, who had been stranded on the island after he was shipwrecked by a dreadful storm. Trinculo stumbled along the beach, looking for somewhere to shelter as the wind whipped around him. The big black clouds above looked like rotten leather bottles that could crack open at any
20   minute. As he searched for a bush or shrub to hide under before the clouds spilt their foul contents on top of him, Trinculo came across a ragged bundle on the ground.

Intrigued, Trinculo peered through the darkness, trying to work out what he had found. It must be some sort of creature, he thought, probably a fish thrown up by the storm. It smelt awful — salty and rotten. Definitely a fish, and most probably a dead one. It smelt so bad that it must have been
25   lying on the beach for some time. Trinculo gave Caliban a sharp prod with his foot. He was shocked to find that the creature was warm. Maybe this was not a fish after all. Trinculo bent down and gingerly lifted up the edge of Caliban's cloak. The creature had legs! Perhaps this rotten fish was actually an islander who had
30   been struck by lightning!

The thunder roared again and a flash of lightning struck close by, illuminating the beach in a blaze of eerie, greenish light. Trinculo glanced about him, but there was no other shelter in sight, only the gloomy beach stretching away into the distance. Trinculo held his
35   nose and crawled under the cloak with Caliban. He would solve the mystery of the strange creature when the storm had passed.

An adapted extract from *The Tempest* by William Shakespeare.

1 What do you learn about the character Prospero in this extract? Explain your answer.

....

....

2 marks

2 In your own words, summarise the key events in lines 16-36.

....

....

2 marks

3 How does the author want you to feel about Caliban? What makes you think this?

....

....

2 marks

4 What impression do you get of the storm in this extract?
How does the author use language to create this impression?

....

....

2 marks

5 Is the style of writing in this extract similar or different to what you
would expect in a play written in the 1600s? Explain your answer.

....

2 marks

....

....

Total out of 10

Extra Activities

*   What do you think will happen next? How might Caliban react to Trinculo crawling under his cloak?
    Remember that he thinks Trinculo is an evil spirit. Write a paragraph describing what might happen.

*   Imagine that you are Caliban. What would you want to happen by the end of the play?
    Discuss your ideas with a partner.

*   Does Caliban remind you of any characters you have read about in other books, or seen on television
    or in a film? In what ways are they similar?

*   Rewrite this extract as a playscript. You'll need to come up with some lines of dialogue for the
    characters to say and some stage directions to explain what they're doing.

Meeting your Favourite Character

By now, you've had plenty of practice at reading texts and answering questions. Now it's time to write your own text, think of some questions and then swap with a friend.

Imagine meeting your favourite character from a book. Write an article about the encounter for a magazine. Remember to include a description of the character and details of your conversation.

Now write some comprehension questions about your article in the blue boxes.

1

....

1 mark

2

....

1 mark

Try to make these questions trickier — they're worth 2 marks each.

3

....

....

2 marks

4

....

....

2 marks

5

....

....

2 marks

6

....

....

2 marks

Now swap with a friend.

Can they answer your questions? Can you answer theirs?

Total
out of 10

Answers

How to mark your answers

- Once you've answered all the questions on a text, you should mark your work. In this section, you'll find sample answers to all of the questions in this book.

- Many of the answers in this section start with "E.g.". This means that the question asked you to give your opinion or explain your own ideas about the text. There isn't one "correct answer" to these questions, and the answers we've given are only a guide. You may have written something a bit different. That's fine, as long as your answer is based on the text and goes into a similar amount of detail to the answer we've provided. If you're unsure whether your answer is correct, you should ask a partner or teacher to look at your work.

- The more marks a question is worth, the more detailed your answer should be. For example, if a question is worth three marks, then you will need to make three separate points, or give three examples from the text. If you have only made one point, you should give yourself one mark.

- When you've finished marking your work, hand it to a partner to check that you have awarded the marks fairly.

- Each set of questions is scored out of ten. Don't forget to add up your marks and write the total in the box above the extra activities.

Total
out of 10

The Kite Rider (pages 2-3)

Author / Source:
Geraldine McCaughrean

Genre:
Fiction — novel extract

1. E.g. It makes the reader interested in the story because they want to know how Haoyou's father lost his soul. The opening suggests that something bad is going to happen, which makes the reader feel uneasy.

2. E.g. The name of the ship was changed to "curry favour with the conquering barbarians", which suggests that the region has been invaded.

3. E.g. overweight; fat; obese

4. E.g. The wind-tester is important to the merchants because it tells them whether they should put their goods on the *Chabi* or not. It is important to the sailors because they won't have any work if the merchants don't use their ship.

5. E.g. When his father falls, Haoyou is worried about his father but also glad that his father might now have to stay at home and miss the voyage. When his father appears on the kite, his emotions change to shock and horror.

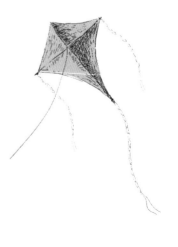

Answers

Pair of Glasses Mistaken for Art (pages 4-5)

Author / Source:
www.theguardian.com

Genre:
Non-fiction — news article

1. E.g. Because some people look at modern art and think "I could have done that". Someone might feel dissatisfied if they travelled to a gallery and didn't find much artistic skill or value in the art they saw there.

2. E.g. Because the glasses weren't actually a piece of art, so they didn't really have any meaning. The author uses the word "probably" to show that she is just making up a possible meaning.

3. E.g. Because a social experiment investigates how people react in different social situations. The prank tested how people behaved in the art gallery and showed that most people assumed the glasses were "art".

4. E.g. The fact that they were taking photos shows that they really believed the glasses were art, so they might have felt shocked when they found out about the prank. They might also have felt embarrassed that they had been tricked.

5. E.g. No, because for something to be art it needs to have been specifically designed and created to be art. The artist needs to have thought about their creation and the kind of message it might send to people when they look at it. OR E.g. Yes, because art is about the way something makes you feel. If something inspires you or makes you think in a new way about something, then it can be considered art.

Wind Cat (pages 6-7)

Author / Source:
Robert Westall

Genre:
Poetry

1. E.g. Because the poem is about how Jeoffrey experiences the wind, and he is also a cat. Comparing the storm to a cat helps the poet to express the wind as Jeoffrey might see it and allows the reader to imagine it from Jeoffrey's perspective.

2. E.g. The wind cat seems huge and terrifying as it can move all over the garden and shake big objects like trees and fences. The wind cat also seems very violent — the poet creates this impression by using words like "assault" and "savagely".

3. E.g. The lines suggest that the cat next door isn't very nice to Jeoffrey and that Jeoffrey is scared of him. The phrase "cat-flap burglar" suggests that the cat sneaks in through the flap when Jeoffrey isn't guarding it.

4. E.g. Jeoffrey is not adventurous. Even though he listens to the wind cat and "suspects a con", he doesn't go outside to investigate it. He is also cowardly — instead of tackling the wind cat by the cat flap, he finds a safe spot by the fire where there's only an "infinitely smaller wind cat".

5. E.g. Using free verse makes the poem unpredictable. This reflects the storm's unpredictable movements, such as the way the wind suddenly moves from the garden to attack the cat flap.

Answers

The Secret Garden
(pages 8-9)

Author / Source:
Frances Hodgson Burnett

Genre:
Classic fiction — novel extract

1. E.g. Mrs Medlock is wearing a bonnet, which is an item of clothing that people don't wear anymore. She works as a housekeeper for Mr Craven, and few people have housekeepers today. Some of the language used, like "pettish" and "railway carriage", is also old fashioned.

2. E.g. The description of Mary makes her sound plain and miserable, and her hair is described as "limp" which means that it looks lifeless. Normally, heroines are described very positively, but Mary sounds boring and not very likeable.

3. E.g. Mrs Medlock thinks that Mary is spoilt, which suggests that she doesn't like Mary very much. She also thinks that Mary is strange because she sits "so still". She compares Mary to an "old woman", which shows that she doesn't think Mary acts like a normal child.

4. E.g. Mary means that she doesn't have a choice about going to live with her uncle now that her parents have died, so it doesn't matter what he is like. It could also mean that Mary is so upset about the death of her parents that nothing matters to her now.

5. E.g. They both have quite cold personalities. Neither of them are close to their family, and they don't seem upset about the death of Mary's parents. They are both unfriendly towards Mrs Medlock — Mary doesn't want to be seen with her and Mr Craven gives her orders without thinking about how they affect her life.

A Letter to The Explorers
Club (pages 10-11)

Author / Source:
Carl Sagan

Genre:
Non-fiction — letter

1. E.g. Yes, because wanting to explore and discover leads people to travel all over the world, even to remote and dangerous places, and this helps us to understand the world better. It has also led to other important human achievements like space exploration. OR E.g. No, because humans have many other characteristics that are more important. I think that creativity is humans' most important characteristic because it leads people to create beautiful things, such as art and music, which bring a lot of happiness into the world.

2. E.g. If men don't let women join then it is men who will miss out. This is because they will not be able to share women's knowledge and discoveries, which will make it harder to keep exploring and learning about the world.

3. E.g. He includes a long list of women who have made important discoveries. This shows that women are making vital contributions in lots of different areas. He also reminds the members of the original reason why the club was founded and tries to make them feel guilty for forgetting this purpose.

4. E.g. Yes, because Carl includes so many examples of women's work that it is impossible to ignore how important they are. He also reminds members of the club's original purpose, which I think the other members would also want to return to. OR E.g. No, because I think some members of the club would have been angry that Carl wanted to change their traditions. Some of them might still have believed that "exploration was not what women did" and might have wanted to stop them from joining the club.

5. E.g. Because it reminds the reader that men and women are part of the same species and have more similarities than differences. This supports Carl's argument that women should be treated equally and given the same opportunities as men.

Answers

Miss Peregrine's Home for Peculiar Children (pages 12-13)

Author / Source: Ransom Riggs

Genre: Fiction — novel extract

1. "branches spindling up like the tips of wet paintbrushes"

2. E.g. Yes, because the metaphor of the house as a "monster" creates a very clear picture. The "vacant hunger" of the house suggests that the house is dangerous and might eat the narrator. This makes the house seem unwelcoming and scary.

3. E.g. Jacob tells himself that someone could still be living in the house because people sometimes live in derelict houses without anybody realising.

4. E.g. Jacob is brave because he enters the house even though it scares him. He is also determined because he has travelled around the world and he isn't going to give up now.

5. E.g. Nature seems wild and uncontrollable — the path has disappeared under "carpets of ivy". The author also says that vines "gnawed at the walls", which makes nature seem destructive. The idea that nature has "waged a war" against the house makes it seem violent.

Through My Eyes (pages 14-15)

Author / Source: Ruby Bridges

Genre: Non-fiction — autobiography

1. E.g. Because Ruby was the first black child to go to the school. This was an important moment that people all over the country would probably have wanted to hear about. The reporters may also have wanted to speak to the protestors and record the events of the protest as they happened.

2. E.g. To stop going somewhere or doing something as a sign of protest.

3. E.g. The owners of a grocery store stopped serving Ruby's family and her father lost his job. I think people did this because they didn't want Ruby's school to be integrated. They may have hoped that if they made life difficult, Ruby's parents would give up and stop sending her to the school.

4. E.g. Because they supported integration. They probably knew that it was really difficult for Ruby and her family to send her to that school. I think they wanted to encourage Ruby and her family and show their support so that they wouldn't give up.

5. E.g. Although the school was supposed to be integrated, there were no white children in Ruby's class and she was taught on her own by Mrs Henry.

Answers

Myths from Different Cultures (pages 16-17)

Author / Source: Zoe Fenwick

Genre: Myths

1. E.g. Yes, because she had become so arrogant about her own skills that she was disrespectful and rude to the gods. OR E.g. No, because Arachne's work was better than Athena's. She shouldn't have been punished when she actually won the contest.

2. E.g. No, because it wasn't a fair competition. Olokun should have won because she had the greatest weaving skills. She only lost because Olodumare tricked her. OR E.g. Yes, because Olokun picked a contest that she knew she would be able to win, so the contest wasn't fair to begin with. It was clever of Olodumare to find a way of using her skill against her.

3. E.g. They are similar because they aren't very honest — they don't act fairly in the contests. Olodumare tricks Olokun, and Athena punishes Arachne even though she won the contest. They are different because Olodumare is more cunning. He takes time to think of a clever plan, but Athena just tries to beat Arachne in a direct competition.

4. E.g. Similar, because they both show that if you have a great talent, you shouldn't become arrogant or conceited about it. Both myths show that people who become too arrogant will be punished or taught a lesson.

5. E.g. They are both short and quickly jump to the action of the myth. Neither of the myths provide much detail about the setting and they give very little information about the characters' lives.

Journey to the Centre of the Earth (pages 18-19)

Author / Source: Jules Verne (adapted)

Genre: Classic fiction — novel extract

1. E.g. The narrator approaches the big hole and looks down into it. He feels scared and starts to think that he is being pulled into the hole. He is about to fall in when he is rescued by Hans.

2. E.g. Yes, because it helps me to imagine what the inside of the shaft looks like. The words "wild and savage" show how scary the shaft looks and how dangerous the climb down is going to be.

3. E.g. He means that they are going so deep down into the Earth that the light from the surface won't reach them any more. The place they are entering is always dark so it seems as if it is always night-time there.

4. E.g. Yes, because he is obviously scared of going into the hole. He calls it a "horrible abyss" and says they are going to face "terrifying dangers". It is very brave of him to climb into the hole when he finds it so frightening. OR E.g. No, because he feels scared all the time. For example, just looking into the hole makes him shake "uncontrollably". A brave person wouldn't find the journey so frightening.

5. E.g. Yes, because it seems like an exciting story. I want to know what happens when the group reach the bottom of the shaft, and I would also like to know why Axel and the Professor decided to go on a journey to the centre of the Earth in the first place.

Answers

The Real Junk Food Project (pages 20-21)

Author / Source:
www.bigissue.com

Genre:
Non-fiction — news article

1. E.g. Yes, because they use food that would otherwise be wasted. It's a good idea for them to be "pay as you feel" because this means that anyone can afford to have a good meal, even if they don't have very much money.

2. E.g. Because the phrase "hard to digest" has two meanings — it can mean that something is hard to believe or that a food is hard for the body to process. The author uses this phrase as a pun because the article is talking about food waste.

3. E.g. It suggests that people don't just use the market stalls because they have to — some people choose to use them. This could be because the food they sell is very good.

4. E.g. The project has led to improved reading, writing and behaviour from pupils. It has also encouraged parents to become more involved with schools, and has given schools extra money from the market stalls.

5. E.g. Adam would like to expand the project nationally or even internationally. He hopes it will change attitudes to food and reduce the use of foodbanks. He is optimistic about the future — he says the project "could have a massive impact".

The Three Musketeers (pages 22-23)

Author / Source:
Alexandre Dumas
Adapted by Ken Ludwig

Genre:
Fiction — playscript

1. E.g. It might be difficult for the actors to get up onto the stage while having a sword fight. It would also be difficult to put the set in place with the actors moving around and fighting on the stage.

2. E.g. The opening fight is very dramatic — the stage directions tell the actors to "fight furiously". This is a big contrast with the friendly dialogue between the characters. The sudden change could be confusing for the audience, but they would also find it funny when they realise the characters are related.

3. E.g. I think that some of the advice is good because it encourages d'Artagnan to stay true to himself and stand up for what he believes in, which is very important. However, some of the advice is bad, such as telling him to kill someone who insults him twice.

4. "thread the needle of Paris"

5. E.g. They have a good relationship because d'Artagnan is learning to fight from his father. D'Artagnan respects his father because he listens to his father's warning about the Cardinal even though he doesn't agree with him. D'Artagnan feels "Overwhelmed" when his father gives him his sword, which shows it is important to both men. The gift suggests respect, trust and love between the characters.

Answers

Penguins Around the World (pages 24-25)

Author / Source:
Zoe Fenwick

Genre:
Non-fiction — reference text

1. "these birds are also highly skilled disco dancers". E.g. Because it is easy to imagine a person dancing, so this metaphor helps the reader to imagine how the penguins move.

2. E.g. alliteration and simile

3. E.g. This paragraph suggests that macaroni penguins are aggressive and violent because they don't nest peacefully together. Instead, they wrestle and hit each other with their flippers.

4. E.g. Life is difficult for African penguins because they have to find somewhere in the shade to build their nests. If their droppings are stolen by humans, they will try to nest under rocks or bushes, but if there is no space they have to nest out in the open.

5. E.g. I think the author writes like this to make the text funny and interesting. It is very different to other non-fiction texts, which makes the reader want to read on.

Anne of Green Gables (pages 26-27)

Author / Source:
Lucy Maud Montgomery (adapted)

Genre:
Classic fiction — novel extract

1. E.g. No, because she lists lots of reasons why Marilla shouldn't adopt Anne. For example, she points out that Marilla doesn't have any experience with children and that she doesn't know what Anne is like.

2. "hair as red as carrots"

3. E.g. No, because she is very rude to Anne and speaks about her as though she's not in the room. She doesn't care about upsetting other people which suggests that she would be difficult to get on with.

4. E.g. The extract ends dramatically and the reader doesn't know how the characters are going to react. This makes the reader want to continue reading to find out what will happen next.

5. E.g. It tells me that Anne is very short-tempered and gets angry very quickly. She is also bold because she shouts at Mrs Rachel without thinking about the trouble she might get into. It also tells me that she is sensitive about how she looks because Mrs Rachel's comments hurt her feelings.